RISE #1

DOUBLE TAKE

SISTER'S KEEPER

$2.50   COAST | McCOMSEY | TIEDE | JEMAS | MANFREDI

	1966	2015
WORLD POPULATION	3,400,000,000	7,200,000,000
McDonald's		
LOCATIONS	850	36,000
COUNTRIES	1	118
BIGGEST BURGER	1.6oz	5.4oz
AVERAGE MEAL CALORIES	590	1,500
Walmart		
LOCATIONS	24	11,495
COUNTRIES	1	28
PERCENTAGE OF PRODUCTS MADE IN CHINA	0%	70%
NFL		
SUPER BOWL VIEWERS	50,000,000	114,000,000
AVERAGE SALARY	$15,000	$1,900,000
Apple		
LOCATIONS	0	453
iOS DEVICES SOLD	0	1,000,000,000
Prison Industry		
STATE AND FEDERAL PRISON POPULATION	200,000	2,300,000
PERCENTAGE OF FEDERAL PRISON POPULATION: DRUG VIOLATIONS	11%–16%	50%
Health Industry		
COST OF HEALTH CARE	$201 PER CAPITA	$10,000 PER CAPITA
COST OF MEDICARE	$3,000,000,000	$634,300,000,000
Political Industry		
COST OF PRESIDENTIAL CAMPAIGN	$8,800,000	$5,000,000,000

STORY
BILL JEMAS
MICHAEL COAST

SCRIPT
MICHAEL COAST
JEFF McCOMSEY

LAYOUTS
KURT TIEDE

PENCILS
FEDERICA MANFREDI

COLORS
VLADIMIR POPOV

COVER
APPLE QINGYANG ZHANG

LETTERS
DARREN SANCHEZ
ELYSIA LIANG

EDITOR
ELYSIA LIANG

DOUBLE TAKE

RICHARD BROOKS | PRODUCTION ASSISTANT
MICHAEL COAST | STORY EDITOR
CLAIRE DRANGINIS | PRODUCTION COORDINATOR
CAROLINE FLANAGAN | PRODUCTION ASSISTANT
ALLISON GADSDEN | EDITORIAL INTERN
WILLIAM GRAVES | DIGITAL PRODUCTION ARTIST
CHARLOTTE GREENBAUM | EDITORIAL ASSISTANT

YOUNG HELLER | STORYBOARD ILLUSTRATOR
BILL JEMAS | GENERAL MANAGER
ELYSIA LIANG | EDITORIAL ASSISTANT
ROBERT MEYERS | MANAGING EDITOR
JULIAN ROWE | STORYBOARD ILLUSTRATOR
LILLIAN TAN | BUSINESS MANAGER
GABE YOCUM | SALES & MARKETING COORDINATOR

Rise #1. September 2015. Published by Double Take, LLC, a subsidiary of Take-Two Interactive Software, Inc. Office of publication: 38 W. 39 Street, 2nd Floor, New York, NY 10018. ©2015 Take-Two Interactive Software, Inc. All Rights Reserved. Printed in Canada.

Is there any of that candy left?

No.

Look at this thing. *"We still remember."*

I don't.

You know, I don't even remember what the man looked like.

...coming back on air after an interruption...

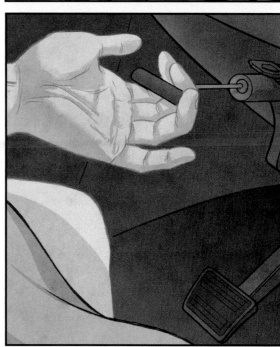

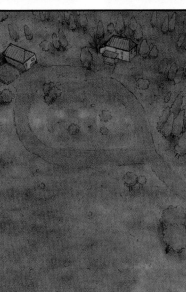

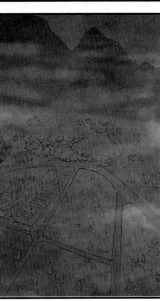

Stay...

BACK!

Saints preserve us!

—braaa...

Government spokesmen warn that dead bodies will continue to be transformed into the flesh-eating ghouls.

All persons who die during this crisis, from whatever cause, will come back to life to seek human victims...

Let go of me!

I came to get you, Barbara.

Johnny... you're—

Yeah, barely.

They said you were dead.

Who said that?

These people. They...

... Johnny!

Look out!

About your car...

...cannot confirm at this time whether this spike in radiation is connected with the Venus Probe.

Could you turn up the radio?

Government officials continue to advise anyone in the area to make their way to a local rescue station.

This is Samantha Stanton from the station that's first on your dial, KBRF 530. Now here's Steve Maserati in DC with...

Is that the same guy who knocked you down?

I slipped.

Why is he following us?

I think he's following YOU.

Hold on.

Do you have any of that candy left?

No.

Really?

I want to try something.

Let me see...

Here.

Go get it!

Look. It's working.

He's hungry.

Come on. Let's get out of here before he gets an appetite again.

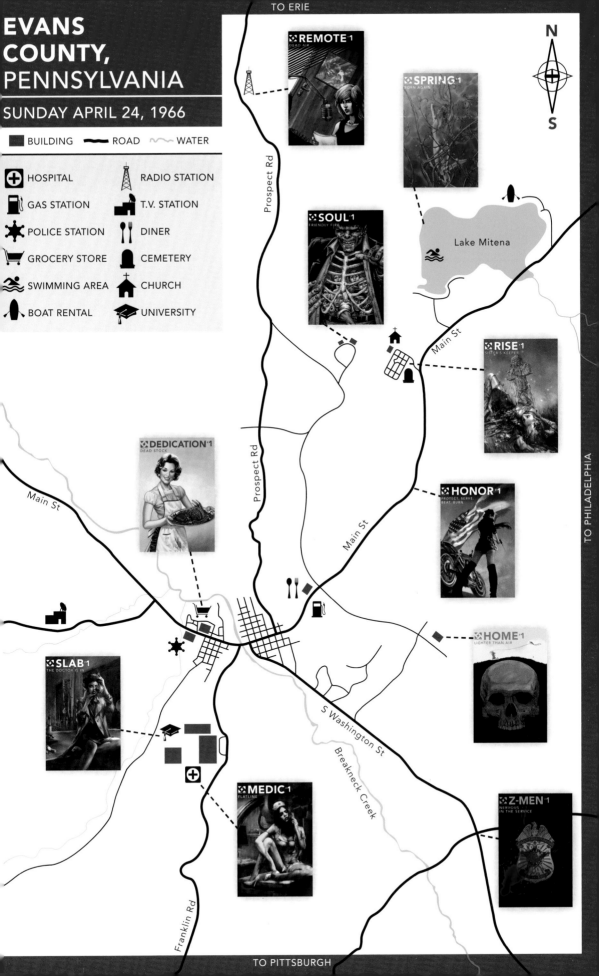

SID MEIER'S CIVILIZATION®
BEYOND EARTH™

WWW.CIVILIZATION.COM